STUDY

THE
JORDAN RIVER
RULES

JOURNEY FROM
TRANSITION TO TRIUMPH

BASED ON THE JORDAN RIVER RULES BY
ROBERT J. MORGAN

Cover Design by Brandon Riesgo

Published by Cover to Cover LLC
Paperback ISBN: 978-0-9884966-8-2

First Edition

Printed in the United States.

CONTENTS

INTRODUCTION

All of us have gone (or will go) through a Red Sea experience. For those not familiar with the story, in the book of the Bible called "Exodus" God called a man named Moses to lead His people out of slavery in Egypt. Through a series of miraculous events, Moses marched multitudes of Hebrew people, the Israelites, away from their captors. But the Pharaoh of Egypt hardened his heart, changed his mind, and geared up to attack and re-capture the Israelites as they were trapped between the Egyptian army and the Red Sea. In the hallmark miracle of the Old Testament, God parted the waters of the Red Sea for the Israelites to walk through safely to the other side. When the Egyptians pursued them, the waters crashed down on their troops and chariots. God made a way when there seemed to be no way.

My father-in-law, Robert J. Morgan (we'll call him "Rob" in this study guide), was reading this story from Exodus on a plane in the late `90s while he himself was in great distress, facing a Red Sea experience. Over the years he's recounted many times that it was as if God Himself was in the seat next to him, teaching him 10 "Red Sea Rules," strategies for difficult times. Rob says he could barely write as quickly as the principles poured forth from the story. Rob's book, *The Red Sea Rules* was published in 2001, and the next two decades would see hundreds of thousands of people impacted.

Several years ago a friend of Rob's and mine named Ted Squires suggested that Rob should write a sequel to *The Red Sea Rules*, without knowing what that would be. Rob and I discussed this as a great idea, but didn't want to force anything. A couple years later, reading through Joshua, it hit me: there is a sequel to the Red Sea story in Scripture. The Red Sea was not the only water that was parted, allowing the Israelites passage. When Moses died, his protégé Joshua was told to take up the mantle. Where Moses had led the Israelites away from danger, Joshua was to lead them into victory. Moses fled from the enemy; Joshua was to conquer the enemy. This time, God led Joshua and the Israelites to the Jordan River, where again the waters were parted. The same God who led them out of Egypt would lead them on to the Promised Land! I encouraged Rob to begin praying and studying this section of Scripture, and that's how The Jordan River Rules book was born.

Don't miss the significance here! We all experience intense panic. But we're also meant to experience the victory that comes with moving forward in God's timing. He provides for both!

This study guide will accompany *The Jordan River Rules* book, walking you through very practical implications and application of this scriptural account.

Wandering

We all face Red Sea panic, but what about the rest of life? Not all of life is traumatic. In fact, sometimes it can seem like walking on a treadmill—not really getting anywhere meaningful. Two of my friends on separate occasions lamented, "Sometimes life feels like the movie *Groundhog Day*; it's just the same drudgery all the time." I was amazed they both used the same example. The repetition of life can leave us feeling like we're wandering around in circles. We feel aimless, purposeless, and confused about our ultimate destination. How can we press forward in a meaningful way? That's a major focus of this study.

For an entire 40 years before Joshua was commissioned as Moses' successor and the Jordan River was parted, the Israelites were wandering in the desert as a consequence of their disbelief. Despite all the miracles of protection and provision, they didn't ultimately believe that God would fulfill His promise to make them victorious over their enemies and allow them to take possession of the land He'd promised centuries before. After the unbelieving generation died off, the Jordan River would become the place where everything changed—a new phase in moving forward in victory after decades of wandering.

Maybe you feel stuck in an unfulfilling job, a mundane project that seems it will never end, or some other drudgery or immobilizing situation, wishing you could move forward. If so, what are you experiencing? If you *don't* feel this way, is there an area where you wish you could move forward and experience victory? Explain your "Jordan River" situation below.

_____

_____

_____

_____

Wondering

What must it have been like for Joshua, after wandering with the rebellious Israelites for 40 years, to be told by God that it's time to move forward? Life had been the same for four decades! All of a sudden it was drastically different. That's why transition is a major theme of this book and study—it's wrought with challenges that can shock our senses.

Just before Rob wrote this book, his wife of 43 years (my mother-in-law) passed away after a long battle with multiple sclerosis. Talk about a transition! Whether through the death of a loved one, a change in school or career, a new relationship or marriage, a lost relationship or divorce, a new baby or stage of a kid's life, a new era of aging or caretaking, etc.—transitions are hard! We're left wondering how to adapt, often worried about how things will turn out for the better.

Perhaps you're experiencing a major transition in life, having difficulty moving forward. If so, explain:

_____

_____

_____

_____

_____

_____

_____

Whatever you wrote above in either or both blank spaces may help focus your application of the Jordan River Rules material. Whether you're wandering, wondering, or simply wanting victory in your life's circumstances—let's move forward together!

Let's Go!

The Jordan River Rules include 10 principles we can apply as steps forward:

1. Realize God Means for You to Move Forward
2. Say No to Discouragement, Yes to Strength
3. Step Up to the Moment
4. Find Someone to Help Along the Way
5. Expect God to Guide You Where You've Never Been Before
6. Prepare Today for Tomorrow's Wonders
7. Trust God to Turn Problems into Pathways
8. Build a Monument
9. You're Not in Charge, But Remember Who Is
10. Encircle Obstacles with Biblical Faith and Shout the Victory

With each step as a lesson, we'll follow this pattern:

One of my best friends is in his 70s, a former military sites preservation specialist for the Tennessee State Historical Commission. I had no idea until he told me recently that there's a federal "Office of the Historian," which functions partly to help presidents and other federal officials make decisions about the future based on lessons learned from the past (visit history.state.gov/about to learn more; it's fascinating!). In the "look backward" section we'll do something similar; we'll review especially the Israelites' journey to extrapolate timeless principles.

After identifying timeless principles, we must also be introspective. How can we apply scriptural principles we've learned to our own core motivations? How can we be corrected, encouraged, changed? In the "look inward" section, we'll focus on aligning ourselves to God's path forward.

Once we've identified and immersed ourselves in scriptural principles as they apply to the core of our being, we can confidently apply truths to our specific situations. We'll ask ourselves questions about how what we've learned can carry us forward toward a victorious future.

In Joshua 4 (and in rule 8) we'll look at the Israelites' memorial stones, stones they pulled from the Jordan River as a monument for future generations, memorializing what the Lord did. Journaling is one way to memorialize God's activity in your life. Space will be provided at the end of this study guide where you can journal each step of the way.

A final note about these sections: not everyone learns the same way. It's extremely helpful for some to review and write out answers to all the questions. Others may wish to simply use the blank spaces to answer with quick shorthand notes. That's okay. I'd encourage you to use the questions fully for at least one or two rules, then see what fits your learning style the best. The most important thing is to absorb the scripture, identify timeless principles, and apply them to your life. Review and writing can help cement information in your mind, so make use of this study guide however is most practical.

Ready? Let's get going and begin by praying and affirming with the psalmist:

Lord...you hold my future.

Psalm 16:5

RULE #1

Realize God Means for You to Move Forward

 LOOK BACKWARD

Read Joshua 1:1–2

These two simple verses are full of context and meaning. What makes this situation so intense for Joshua?

Moses' died + Joshua needs to lad The Israelites across the river

Now read Joshua 1:1–5

Rob suggests that this passage provides three truths about God's guidance:

1.   He leads us in _Stages_
2.   He leads us in _Steps_
3.   He leads us in _Person_

Read Numbers 33:1–2 and Psalm 84:5–7.

What word or idea shows up in these passages, and what does it teach us about God's direction?

How does Philppians 3:13–15 teach us to move forward?

_____

_____

_____

_____

_____

One rule that sticks with me from *The Red Sea Rules* was "Take the next logical step by faith." The same theme shows up in Joshua, where we learn that God leads us step by step. What insight do Psalm 119:105, Psalm 139:16 and Ephesians 2:10 add to this principle?

_____

_____

_____

_____

Rob finishes rule #1 by highlighting that God leads us in a very personal way. Read the following scriptures and make notes on anything that stands out to you after reading them all:

- Joshua 1:5

- Deuteronomy 31:6–8

- 1 Chronicles 28:20

- Psalm 27:9

_____

_____

_____

_____

🔍 LOOK INWARD

Rob recounts the death of his wife, Katrina, saying: "I'm aware my life is entering a new phase, and I'm reminded life unfolds in stages." Are you entering a new phase or stage of life, or would you like to? Explain:

_____

_____

_____

_____

_____

I'm a big-picture thinker. I tend to lose the forest for the trees and often become paralyzed when a project or situation seems too big to tackle. Do you have similar struggles? How do you feel overwhelmed right now?

_____

_____

_____

_____

Reflecting on the biblical principle that God leads you in person:

Have you experienced this truth in the past? If so, in what situation?

_____

_____

_____

_____

_____

Do you have difficulty believing or experiencing God's presence in your current situation? If so, can you articulate why, and identify anything that may help?

_____

_____

_____

_____

_____

MOVE FORWARD

What's your biggest hindrance to applying Rule #1: Realize God means for you to move forward? Circle any that apply (or write in your own):

Apathy	Pain
Disbelief	Fear
Shame	Discouragement
Obstacles	Stubborness
Laziness	Distractions

_____

_____

_____

_____

_____

_____

How can what you've read and internalized here help you move forward? Be specific:

_____

_____

_____

_____

 JOURNAL

The journal space for Rule #1 is provided at the end of this study guide and is very important at this stage. Hopefully you'll see where you started, your struggles, your progress, and your victories later on.

Heavenly Father,

I believe You mean for me to move forward. If I'm stuck as a consequence of my action or inaction, help me out of any unhealthy or sinful patterns. I believe You've laid out the stages of my life, every step I can take, and that You Yourself will be with me. Be with me now and help me move forward.

In Jesus' name, amen.

> *...And remember, I am with you always, to the end of the age.*
>
> *Matthew 18:20*

RULE #2

Say No to Discouragement, Yes to Strength

LOOK BACKWARD

Joshua 1:9 perhaps is some of the strongest encouragement anywhere in Scripture. What elements do you notice from this passage?

_____

_____

_____

_____

Rob spells out all thirty times in Scripture where God commands His people to be strong. As you read these, which instance(s) speaks to you most personally?

_____

_____

_____

_____

Read Numbers 13:27–31. Joshua was one of two spies who came back without fear of the enemy while the other ten discouraged the Israelites. What punishment did this lead to for the Israelites, and what principles does it teach us about fear, discouragement, and unbelief?

_____

_____

_____

Read Matthew 6:34 and John 16:33. What principles stand out to you?

_____

_____

_____

_____

Rob says, "The Bible has nothing good to say about discouragement. Not one word." Read the following passages, or re-read the first couple pages of the "Do Not Be Discouraged" section in Rule #2:

- 1 Samuel 17:32

- 1 Chronicles 20:15-17, 22:13, 28:20, 32:7

- Isaiah 42:4

- Ezekiel 2:6

- Ephesians 3:13

- 1 Thessalonians 5:14

What additional insights do these passages shed on discouragement?

_____

_____

_____

LOOK INWARD

Again Rob recounts his experience with Katrina's death. He notes needing to be strong for his family and for her. What situation are you facing that requires strength?

_____

_____

_____

How can, should, or did the 30 passages on strength impact you in your situation now?

_____

_____

_____

_____

Which tends to affect you more (circle one):

Fear   Discouragement   Disbelief

If you're experiencing a transition, or want to, what fears accompany these changes? How does the command "do not be afraid" impact you?

_____

_____

_____

_____

If you're feeling discouraged, write (as if talking to a friend) why:

_____

_____

_____

_____

MOVE FORWARD

Rob makes several suggestions to help you choose through grace to be enthusiastic. Choose one (or write in your own idea):

1.   Write a different verse atop every page of your calendar.

2.   Learn some of them by heart.

3.   Meditate on them.

4.   Weave them into your thoughts until they animate your personality.

5.   _____

Rob ends this rule by making three suggestions to galvanize against discouragement. Re-read if necessary and make notes on how you can apply each:

Resignation

_____

_____

_____

_____

_____

Recalibration

_____

_____

_____

_____

Recalculation

_____

_____

_____

_____

_____

JOURNAL

Journal space for Rule #2 is provided at the end of this study guide. Take some time to journal your thoughts and experience through this step.

Heavenly Father,

Thank You for both commanding and providing strength. Help me say no to fear and discouragement and yes to strength.

In Jesus' name, amen.

> *May...your strength last as long as you live.*
>
> *Deuteronomy 33:25*

RULE #3

Step Up to the Moment

LOOK BACKWARD

Read Joshua 1:11. Imagine yourself among the Israelites, learning that God gave these words to your leader. What elements of this verse stand out to you, considering this context?

_____

_____

_____

_____

_____

Read Numbers 32. Then read Joshua 1:14–16. This fulfillment of a historic promise, a promise made by previous generations, was now being fulfilled. Does this offer any guiding principle for how you operate?

_____

_____

_____

_____

_____

_____

LOOK INWARD

Rob warns, "It's easy to mess up between stages of life." What possible dangers or traps are present in your current stage?

_____

_____

_____

_____

_____

Rob also points out the incredible need for rest before we take major steps. Are you the type of person to "push push push" forward without allowing yourself time to recalibrate? What implications does God-ordained times of rest or preparation have for you?

_____

_____

_____

_____

_____

Using the example of the Reubenites and Gadites, Rob urges us to have the same commitment to God's work: "everything...everywhere." Reflect on one challenge and one victory you've experienced in your attempt to stay committed to the Lord's work.

_____

_____

_____

_____

_____

MOVE FORWARD

This simple rule highlights two main things to help avoid the dangers that lie in wait as we're moving forward: allowing ourselves time for rest and preparation, and committing ourselves exuberantly and completely to the work God has for us.

Make a plan with specificity and practicality as to how you can integrate a time of rest and preparation into your journey forward.

_____

_____

_____

Do you lack zeal or resolute commitment to the future God has for you? Write out a statement of commitment or a prayer of surrender right now:

_____

_____

_____

JOURNAL

Journal space for Rule #3 is provided at the end of this study guide. Take some time to journal your thoughts and experience through this step.

Heavenly Father,

Please help me avoid the dangers and traps that accompany the stage of life I'm in and the one I'm moving toward. Give me the wisdom to know how to integrate rest and preparation into my life, and give me absolute abandon and fervor to follow You anywhere You lead.

In Jesus' name, amen.

Take delight in the Lord, and he will give you your heart's desires.

Psalm 37:4

RULE #4

Find Someone to Help Along the Way

LOOK BACKWARD

Read Joshua 2 (it won't take but a couple minutes!). What's notable to you about this passage?

_____

_____

_____

_____

Read Genesis 15:13–16. In this passage, God tells Abraham it will be four hundred years until the sin of those inhabiting the Promised Land reached its full measure. Then the spies end up being hidden by a prostitute. What principles can you glean from these elements of the story?

_____

_____

_____

_____

Read the following passages:

- Matthew 1:5

- Hebrews 11:31

- James 2:25

What aspects of Joshua 2 are carried through in these passages?

_____

_____

_____

_____

Read Joshua 2:18. The "crimson cord" saved Rahab's family. Although it's not explicit in the passage, there are echoes of the passover that perhaps were intended. Now read Romans 5:9, Ephesians 1:7, Hebrews 9:14, Hebrews 10:19, and 1 Peter 1:19. How might these passages relate to or at least reflect Joshua 2?

_____

_____

_____

_____

LOOK INWARD

Rob says, "As we move into the upcoming stages in our lives, we need to receive and give help, and that's part of our mission." Are you prone to focus too much on yourself in this stage of life, neglecting others? How can the biblical principles from this chapter embed themselves into your nature?

_____

_____

_____

Rahab was a prostitute living in a city sinful enough to warrant God's most extreme judgment. Yet, she was saved. We all tend to shame ourselves. How does Rahab's story encourage you?

_____

_____

_____

The spies found a way to help Rahab who helped them. Are there people in your life helping you that you've neglected to help? Explain / reflect:

_____

_____

_____

_____

_____

Rob relates the "crimson cord" to the passover lamb, ultimately to Christ's blood shed for us. He explains that the "crimson cord" runs throughout Scripture. How often do you reflect on Christ's sacrifice? How does it change your perspective on your current situation?

_____

_____

_____

_____

_____

MOVE FORWARD

Take a moment to think about relationships you have with others. Name a person or two you could help:

_____

_____

_____

_____

How, specifically, could you help them?

_____

_____

_____

_____

Make a solid plan to take action (including when, if possible).

_____

_____

_____

_____

_____

Take a moment right now to do one of the following, to appreciate and act based on Christ's "crimson cord," His blood shed for you:

1. Sing a hymn such as "Are You Washed in the Blood" or "Rock of Ages."

2. If you've not been participating, find out when your church is next serving the Lord's Supper and make plans to go.

3. Memorize one of these verses: Romans 5:9, Ephesians 1:7, Hebrews 9:14, Hebrews 10:19, or 1 Peter 1:19.

4. Write a prayer of thanksgiving for the shed blood of Christ for your sins:

_____

_____

_____

_____

_____

JOURNAL

Journal space for Rule #4 is provided at the end of this study guide. Take some time to journal your thoughts and experience through this step.

Heavenly Father,

Please bless me with others to help me in my journey, but do not let me neglect helping others as well. Show me specific people and situations where I can serve. Thank You for the salvation You offer through the blood of Jesus and the life offered by His resurrection.

In Jesus' name, amen.

Therefore, whatever you want others to do for you, do also the same for them, for this is the Law and the Prophets.

Matthew 7:12

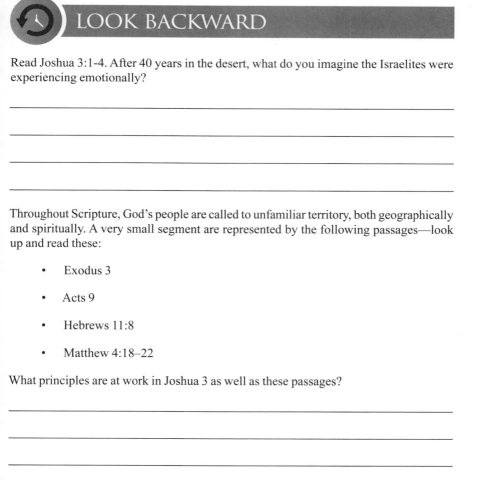

RULE #5

Expect God to Guide You Where You've Never Been Before

LOOK BACKWARD

Read Joshua 3:1-4. After 40 years in the desert, what do you imagine the Israelites were experiencing emotionally?

_____

_____

_____

_____

Throughout Scripture, God's people are called to unfamiliar territory, both geographically and spiritually. A very small segment are represented by the following passages—look up and read these:

- Exodus 3

- Acts 9

- Hebrews 11:8

- Matthew 4:18–22

What principles are at work in Joshua 3 as well as these passages?

_____

_____

_____

_____

19

Read Psalms 25:4–5, 32:8–9, and Psalms 73:23–28. What can you glean from these about the Lord's guidance?

_____

_____

_____

_____

LOOK INWARD

How do you typically respond to new territory? Circle all that apply.

Fear   Courage

Excitement   Anger

Confusion   Timidity

Exhaustion

What situation is specifically causing this reaction from you now (it's okay if this is the same answer as you've given previously—your "Jordan River" situation)?

_____

_____

_____

_____

Why do you think you tend to approach this situation the way you do, whether feeling alone or feeling confident in the Lord's presence?

_____

_____

_____

Rob lays out the path forward in the section titled "Read the Compass." Using the example of the compass, he suggests principles for progress. Let's apply each one.

The center begins with a deep conviction of God's sovereignty. Write a quick prayer or statement of faith asserting your belief in God's control.

_____

_____

_____

_____

The circumference of the compass is wholehearted willingness. Again, assert your surrender to God's direction in your life through a prayer or statement below.

_____

_____

_____

_____

The N stands for Nearness. In what ways has God shown Himself to you through this journey so far?

_____

_____

_____

_____

The S on the dial stands for Scripture. Write out either how you're already involved in a discipline of immersing yourself in Scripture, or a plan to incorporate this discipline.

_____

_____

_____

_____

The E stands for Events and clarifying circumstances. Explain how God has worked in unexpected ways in the past, as well as circumstances that feel uncertain that you'd like clarity in now.

_____

_____

_____

_____

The W represents Weighing the Options. Read Proverbs 16:9 and Psalm 25:4–5. Rewrite one or both in your own words.

_____

_____

_____

_____

JOURNAL

Journal space for Rule #5 is provided at the end of this study guide. Take some time to journal your thoughts and experience through this step.

Heavenly Father,

I surrender myself to Your leading. Although the way may be unknown and fearful to me, I entrust myself to You. Make Your ways known to me and teach me Your path.

In Jesus' name, amen.

> _Make your ways known to me, Lord; teach me your paths. Guide me in your truth and teach me, for...I wait for you all day long._
>
> _Psalm 24:4–5_

RULE #6

Prepare Today for Tomorrow's Wonders

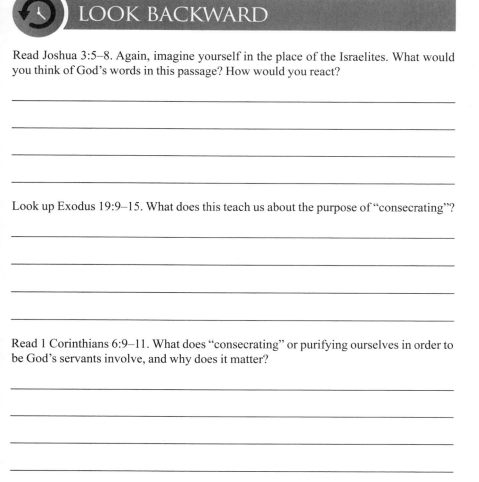

LOOK BACKWARD

Read Joshua 3:5–8. Again, imagine yourself in the place of the Israelites. What would you think of God's words in this passage? How would you react?

_____

_____

_____

_____

Look up Exodus 19:9–15. What does this teach us about the purpose of "consecrating"?

_____

_____

_____

_____

Read 1 Corinthians 6:9–11. What does "consecrating" or purifying ourselves in order to be God's servants involve, and why does it matter?

_____

_____

_____

_____

Read Hebrews 13:12, Ephesians 4:1 and 22–24, and Romans 6:19. What do these passages teach us about the importance of our condition?

_____

_____

_____

_____

What does Colossians 1:29 teach us about the relationship between our labor and His strength?

_____

_____

_____

LOOK INWARD

Do you have a sense of expectation about what the Lord is doing or preparing you for? Why or why not?

_____

_____

_____

_____

Rob explains the difference between our position and our condition. Rewrite the correlation here in your own words.

_____

_____

_____

In light of the New Testament passages we looked at previously, do you feel "consecrated" for your next steps? Why or why not?

_____

_____

_____

MOVE FORWARD

Do you feel the reality of your position in Christ, as sanctified and cleansed? Make a plan below for this coming week to reflect on your position in Christ. Whether it involves daily Scripture reading, memorization or meditation on some of the passages above, detail it here.

_____

_____

_____

Does your position match your condition? If not, write out what areas of your life need work, repentance, or modification. If so, write down some areas where you're victorious and say a prayer of thanksgiving.

_____

_____

_____

What wonders could God do in your life? Take a moment to imagine a brighter future, where God acts mightily. Write a description of what this might look like.

_____

_____

_____

Take a moment to submit yourself to whatever future God has, and to believe He will truly work wonders in your life.

JOURNAL

Journal space for Rule #6 is provided at the end of this study guide. Take some time to journal your thoughts and experience through this step.

Heavenly Father,

Thank You for Jesus. Thank You for making me holy through His finished work on the cross. Today and every day, mold me increasingly into His image. Consecrate me and clean up my life for Your service. Work Your wonders, and let me see Your glory that I may praise You.

In Jesus' name, amen.

> *Now may the God of peace himself sanctify you completely. And may your whole spirit, soul, and body be kept sound and blameless at the coming of our Lord Jesus Christ.*
>
> *1 Thessalonians 5:23*

RULE #7

Trust God to Turn Problems into Pathways

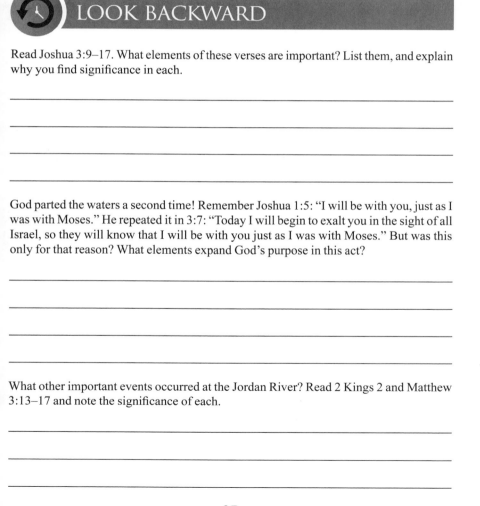

LOOK BACKWARD

Read Joshua 3:9–17. What elements of these verses are important? List them, and explain why you find significance in each.

_____

_____

_____

_____

God parted the waters a second time! Remember Joshua 1:5: "I will be with you, just as I was with Moses." He repeated it in 3:7: "Today I will begin to exalt you in the sight of all Israel, so they will know that I will be with you just as I was with Moses." But was this only for that reason? What elements expand God's purpose in this act?

_____

_____

_____

_____

What other important events occurred at the Jordan River? Read 2 Kings 2 and Matthew 3:13–17 and note the significance of each.

_____

_____

_____

What does Psalm 66:6 indicate an important result of the crossing was?

_____

_____

_____

_____

While God certainly delights in performing miracles for His people, it always aligns with His purposes. That means, not every obstacle results in a miracle. Read Isaiah 43:1–2. Write, in your own words, the three main elements of these verses.

_____

_____

_____

_____

Sometimes, as Rob suggests, we "fall into the river." How does Psalm 18:16 apply to such situations?

_____

_____

_____

_____

LOOK INWARD

How do you typically react when you reach obstacles?

_____

_____

_____

_____

What is the biggest obstacle in your way?

_____

_____

_____

Reading this rule and the passages above, do you have a sense of which applies more? Circle the most applicable option, or write in your own answer.

Experiencing or Expecting a Miracle

The River Isn't Parting

I'm Falling into the River

Explain your situation and why you've answered this way.

_____

_____

_____

MOVE FORWARD

Based on the answer you just circled above in the previous section, take the next few minutes to memorize or meditate on the following verses.

- Experiencing or Expecting a Miracle: Memorize/meditate on Psalm 66:6.

- The River Isn't Parting: Memorize/meditate on Isaiah 43:1–2.

- I'm Falling into the River: Memorize/meditate on Psalm 18:16.

What other practical steps can you take to increase your level of confidence in and dependence on God?

_____

_____

_____

JOURNAL

Journal space for Rule #7 is provided at the end of this study guide. Take some time to journal your thoughts and experience through this step.

Heavenly Father,

The obstacles I face may be daunting, but I choose to trust in You. Please turn my problems into pathways. Yet, not my will but Yours be done. If You don't part the waters, carry me through or lift me out of the flood in Your way. I commit myself into Your keeping.

In Jesus' name, amen.

He turned the sea into dry land, and they crossed the river on foot. There we rejoiced in him.

Psalm 66:6

RULE #8

Build a Monument

Read Joshua 4 and reflect on the chapter. Then answer the following questions.

What's the significance of the number of stones?

_____

_____

_____

_____

Read verses 6–7, then read verse 24 again. List the reasons behind the memorial stones given in the passage.

_____

_____

_____

_____

Read 1 Samuel 7. What elements are similar in this passage, and what do these stories combined teach us about how God urges His people to memorialize His works?

_____

_____

_____

Read Psalm 71:18. Are physical monuments the only way to memorialize God's power? What other way does this Psalm suggest?

_____

_____

_____

_____

LOOK INWARD

What wonders has God worked in your life, recently or long ago in your life? List a few things briefly below.

_____

_____

_____

_____

Have you taken steps to memorialize these events? If so, list how. If not, reflect on why not and whether you wish you had.

_____

_____

_____

_____

Are you prone to tell others stories of God's work, both in history and in your life or the lives of others you know? If so, recall a time you've done so. If not, reflect again as to why this may be difficult for you.

_____

_____

_____

MOVE FORWARD

Rob makes it explicit in this rule how to put this idea into practice. We'll follow these steps, attempting to be precise about our application.

Rob urges us: **First, write your testimony, your story, and an account of your life.** Make a few notes below highlighting what you'd like to touch on. Then take a few moments to put some dates on your calendar to work on these things!

_____

_____

_____

_____

Second, we can leave behind a personal Bible, Rob explains. Again, write down the name or names of a person or people you'd like to leave a personal Bible to. Be very practical here, and go ahead and plan to write this into your will, or at least write a dedication in the front of each Bible and let that person or those people know your intentions.

_____

_____

_____

_____

Finally, Rob tells us that **we leave monuments by what we do with our lives and by what we give.** What people, church, or organizations in your life will be affected by your giving? List them below and ask God to bless and multiply what you're giving for His glory. If you're not currently giving, list some ideas for your giving. Be sure to make some time to act on these ideas this week!

_____

_____

_____

_____

JOURNAL

Journal space for Rule #8 is provided at the end of this study guide. Take some time to journal your thoughts and experience through this step.

Heavenly Father,

You have done and will continue to do great things in my life and in the lives of those I live in community with. Help me and help us to learn how to best memorialize these things. Fill our mouths with words to the next generation that exalt You and preserve the memory of how You've worked in the past.

In Jesus' name, amen.

Even while I am old and gray, God, do not abandon me, while I proclaim your power to another generation, your strength to all who are to come.

Psalm 71:18

RULE #9

You're Not in Charge, But Remember Who Is

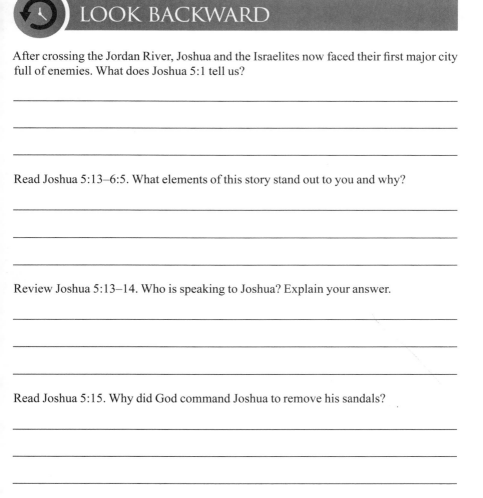

LOOK BACKWARD

After crossing the Jordan River, Joshua and the Israelites now faced their first major city full of enemies. What does Joshua 5:1 tell us?

_____

_____

_____

Read Joshua 5:13–6:5. What elements of this story stand out to you and why?

_____

_____

_____

Review Joshua 5:13–14. Who is speaking to Joshua? Explain your answer.

_____

_____

_____

Read Joshua 5:15. Why did God command Joshua to remove his sandals?

_____

_____

_____

What do you think about the battle plan in Joshua 6:2–5?

_____

_____

_____

_____

Review these other battle plans in Scripture:

- Judges 7

- 1 Samuel 17

- 2 Chronicles 20

- 2 Chronicles 32, 2 Kings 19

What do you think these seemingly odd strategies and actions teach us?

_____

_____

_____

_____

LOOK INWARD

My own tendency, even after a great triumph, is to worry about the next obstacle instead of seeing how God's acting on my behalf in the past affects the future. I wish I could be more like others who seem to move forward from obstacle to obstacle with great confidence. Does this describe you? Why do you think so, or why not?

_____

_____

_____

_____

God spoke to Joshua very directly. How is this scene similar and different from the way you interact with God?

_____

_____

_____

_____

_____

As you've been moving forward in your journey, has anything seemed odd or unexpected, or does your path forward seem obscure? If so, explain.

_____

_____

_____

_____

_____

Have you relinquished control, or are you still trying to take charge yourself? What struggles and victories have you had in this area of your journey?

_____

_____

_____

_____

_____

MOVE FORWARD

One of our most difficult struggles in life is finding the balance between acting when we should and releasing control to God. There's wisdom in the "serenity prayer." Take a moment to pray this now:

God, please grant me the serenity to accept the things I cannot change,
The courage to change the things I can,
And the wisdom to know the difference.

The commander of God's armies appeared to Joshua for the special occasion of moving forward. Have you asked God to make Himself known clearly to you in a sort of "holy meeting"? Explain how this is already part of your life, or how you could integrate more personal interaction with Him.

_____

_____

_____

_____

_____

Take a moment to sing the hymn "A Mighty Fortress" or simply to reflect on its words. The entire hymn is easy to find online or in most hymn books. Here's verse two:

Did we in our own strength confide,
our striving would be losing,
were not the right Man on our side,
the Man of God's own choosing.
You ask who that may be?
Christ Jesus, it is he;
Lord Sabaoth his name,
from age to age the same;
and he must win the battle.

Martin Luther (1529)
Translator: Frederick H. Hedge (1852)

JOURNAL

Journal space for Rule #9 is provided at the end of this study guide. Take some time to journal your thoughts and experience through this step.

Heavenly Father,

You're in charge. I surrender to Your leadership. Please help me know when to wait, when to listen, and when to act. Meet with me, oh Lord of Hosts, and command Your hosts to do Your will, and help me to fall in line with Your battle plan.

In Jesus' name, amen.

> *...for kingship belongs to the Lord; he rules the nations.*
>
> *Psalm 22:28*

RULE #10

Encircle Obstacles with Biblical Faith and Shout the Victory

LOOK BACKWARD

Read Joshua 6. We've now come to the landmark miracle and victory that would set the tone for the Israelites' conquest of the Promised Land. As you read, what elements of the story do you find surprising?

_____

_____

_____

_____

What function do you think these elements of the battle served?

- The ark of the covenant

- The seven priests and the seven shofars

- Silence commanded for six days

- The final shout and rams' horns blowing

Read 2 Corinthians 10:3–5 and Ephesians 6:10–20. Compare and contrast the battle methods of the Israelites with instructions to Christians who follow Christ.

_____

_____

_____

_____

Read the following in Psalms.

Note, in the "move forward" section below, you'll be encouraged to select one or more to memorize / meditate on, so you might want to bookmark these!

- 20:5 *May God grant all your requests*
- 33:3
- 47:5
- 66:1
- 89:15
- 95:2

What timeless principle(s) can we draw from these passages?

Praise Him always no matter what

The city of Jericho was destroyed, but Rahab was spared. Why do you think Rahab's story appears again in this section?

What other elements of the story are notable from which you can draw timeless truths?

LOOK INWARD

Rob writes, "What's keeping you awake at night? Hindering your success? Blocking your way at work or home? That's your Jericho." Perhaps this is the same answer you've given throughout this study guide, or maybe something new has cropped up, or another aspect of your journey presents as Jericho. What's your Jericho?

_____

_____

_____

_____

_____

Are you prone to surrounding your problem with prayer? If so, explain how this process has gone so far. If not, what do you think is keeping you from doing so?

_____

_____

_____

_____

_____

Rob suggests that "victory isn't found in pushing through our own schemes but in cooperating with what He intends to accomplish in His own way and time." What's your honest reaction to this statement, considering your own personal Jericho situation?

Be Still + Wait_____

_____

_____

_____

_____

MOVE FORWARD

Rob again offers very practical steps for this rule, saying, "Whatever your challenge, claim Joshua 3:5 and follow the Jericho pattern."

First, encircle your obstacle with power. Rob suggests power is found "only in the presence of Him who died and rose again for us." What steps can you take, specifically, to spend time in His presence this week?

_____

_____

_____

_____

Second, encircle your obstacle with prayer. How is your prayer life? Consider and place a checkbox by any of the following practical steps you can take, or write in your own ideas.

☐ Put your keys under your bed each night so you remember to get on your knees to pray about your problem each day.

☐ Call or contact at least three friends to ask them for prayer support this week, encircling your problem.

☐ Create a prayer journal and add an entry daily or a few times per week.

(Insert your own ideas below.)

☐

☐

☐

Third, encircle your obstacle with promises. Again, check any ideas you plan to implement, or write in your own.

☐ Look up promises in Scripture that apply to your situation. Write them on sticky notes and place them where you'll see them (on your alarm clock, on your car's dash, on your computer monitor, etc.).

☐ Choose three promises from Scripture to memorize over the course of the next three weeks.

☐ Call or contact three friends (perhaps the same ones praying with you) and ask them to find and share a promise from Scripture with you that pertains to your situation.

(Insert your own ideas below.)

☐

☐

☐

Fourth, encircle your obstacle with perseverance. How can you dedicate yourself to endure? Look up and place a check beside any of the following passages you'd like to memorize or set aside time to meditate on, and write in any other ideas you may have that could help you endure.

☐ Galatians 6:9

☐ Hebrews 12:1

☐ Philippians 4:13

☐ Romans 5:3–4

☐ 2 Corinthians 4:16–18

☐ James 1:2–4

☐ _____ (write in your own if desired)

_____

_____

_____

_____

Fifth, encircle your obstacle with praise. Rob explains his own practice of shouting victoriously (or, at least, working toward it!). Look up (if you didn't already bookmark these as suggested in the Look Inward section above) the following psalms and choose one or more to memorize or meditate on.

Psalms:

☐ 20:5

☐ 33:3

☐ 47:5

☐ 66:1

☐ 89:15

☐ 95:2

☐ _____ (write in your own if desired)

_____

_____

_____

_____

_____

JOURNAL

Journal space for Rule #10 is provided at the end of this study guide. Take some time to journal your thoughts and experience through this step.

Heavenly Father,

Thank you for guiding me through this journey. You're the God who parts waters, tears down walls, defeats evil, and guides me onward. Please continue to guide and bless me with your presence.

In Jesus' name, Amen.

The Lord advances like a warrior; he stirs up his zeal like a soldier. He shouts, he roars aloud, he prevails over his enemies.

Isaiah 42:13

A FINAL WORD

Rob ends the book with a hopeful eye toward heaven, where he says he's got "people up there." Katrina, his wife and my mother-in-law, was an inspiration to tens of thousands of people. She and Rob co-wrote *The Strength You Need,* exploring the Bible's great "strength" passages. Let me tell you something: that woman was a pillar of strength. *The Red Sea Rules* was also dedicated to her two decades ago. In an interesting twist of providence, many victims of hurricane Katrina saw Rob's dedication and wondered if the book was dedicated to Katrina victims. It prompted perhaps many more readers with a timely message. Two decades later, and after her passing, Rob dedicated *The Jordan River Rules* to Katrina as well.

Rob has fought his way through the principles in this book. I've been his closest friend for a long time, which isn't common among in-laws! I've seen his setbacks and victories firsthand as he's transitioned into life without his precious wife. He's also transitioned from being a full-time senior pastor to becoming the preaching pastor, mentoring new leaders and graciously stepping back from his previous role for the good of the church he's served for over 40 years. It's been a struggle, but by God's grace, he's put his heart and soul into the content you've read in *The Jordan River Rules.* Meanwhile, he's continued writing, created a podcast, and continued traveling and speaking all over the country and overseas with tremendous energy.

Could I ask you a favor? Would you pray for Rob? He's great at a lot of things, but I believe God's greatest ministry for him is in the area of Bible teaching, and that perhaps his greatest impact still lies ahead. We're working on a project called "Cover to Cover," which will be Rob's summary of all 66 books of the Bible in 66 teaching segments of 30–45 minutes each. He's also working on a course called "Buck Hatch's Progress of Redemption," which uniquely unfolds and illustrates the big story of the Bible in understandable parts and a beautiful progression.

These projects can't continue aside from the support and prayers of people like you. If you'd like to access more of Pastor Morgan's materials, here are a few great things you can access at robertjmorgan.com:

- Additional books and study guides / materials

- Visit robertjmorgan.com/podcast for his free weekly Bible-teaching podcast content

- Visit robertjmorgan.com/resources to sign up for a free daily devotional with a story matching the calendar day from church history and for many other free downloads

- Online video courses, including "50 Final Events in World History: The Book of Revelation Demystified," a course on the great hymns of the faith, and many more in this growing library

- Sign up for his newsletter to be notified of new material or upcoming events

Now may the God of peace, who brought up from the dead our Lord Jesus— the great Shepherd of the sheep—through the blood of the everlasting covenant, equip you with everything good to do his will, working in us what is pleasing in his sight, through Jesus Christ, to whom be glory forever and ever. Amen.

Hebrews 13:20–21

JOURNAL

RULE #1

Rule #2

_____

_____

_____

_____

_____

_____

_____

_____

_____

_____

_____

_____

_____

_____

_____

_____

_____

_____

_____

_____

_____

_____

_____

_____

RULE #3

_____

_____

_____

_____

_____

_____

_____

_____

_____

_____

_____

_____

_____

_____

_____

_____

_____

_____

_____

_____

_____

_____

_____

_____

_____

_____

_____

RULE #4

RULE #5

Rule #6

RULE #7

RULE #8

RULE #9

RULE #10

_____

_____

_____

_____

_____

_____

_____

_____

_____

_____

_____

_____

_____

_____

_____

_____

_____

_____

_____

_____

_____

_____

ADDITIONAL NOTES